I can sail, like mighty ships.
Like the oceans, I run deep.

I can stretch, just like the Alps,

until I <u>reach</u> my hi<u>gh</u>es<u>t</u> peak.

I can charge, just like a train.
Like a rocket, I'll ignite.

GRACE BYERS

I Believe I Can

PICTURES BY **KETURAH A. BOBO**

SCHOLASTIC INC.

ISBN 978-1-338-69218-1

Text copyright © 2020 by Grace Byers. Illustrations copyright © 2020 by Art by Keturah Ariel LLC.
All rights reserved. Published by Scholastic Inc., 557 Broadway, New York, NY 10012,
by arrangement with Balzer + Bray, an imprint of HarperCollins Children's Books,
a division of HarperCollins Publishers. SCHOLASTIC and associated logos are
trademarks and/or registered trademarks of Scholastic Inc.

The publisher does not have any control over and does not assume any
responsibility for author or third-party websites or their content.

12 11   22 23 24 25 26

Printed in the U.S.A.   40

First Scholastic printing, January 2021

Typography by Jenna Stempel-Lobell

To us all:
There will always be one person
who might not believe in you;
let that person never be you. X
—G.B.

To my brothers, Jaryah and Shamir,
and all those who believe in love and optimism
despite the world making you feel as though you cannot
—K.B.

Like a star, I can project
my brightest shine against the night.

I am like the lion's roar.

I am like a dragon's flames.

I'm worthy because I'm me,

and there is value to my name.

I can build, just like a brick.

I keep going, like a clock.

I can hold, just like cement.
I can last, just like a rock.

Grounded firm, I'm like the soil.
Like the sky, I'm boundless too.

When I believe in myself,
there's simply nothing I can't do.

Like the hero, I am brave
and face my fears despite my fright.
Because I know I'm not alone,
and in the end, I'll be all right.

Sometimes I am right,
and sometimes I am wrong.

But even when I make mistakes,
I learn from them to make me strong.

I may not win at all I do.
I may experience defeat.

But I'll dust off and try again
to be the best that I can be.

I know my power lies within.

There's nothing that
can hold me down.

There is light within my smile.

There is voice within my sound.

My presence matters in this world.
My life is worthy; there's a plan.

I know I can do anything,

if only
I believe
I can.